BRER RABBIT
AND THE HONEY POT
AND
BRER RABBIT AND BRER BEAR

Illustrated by Lesley Smith

AWARD PUBLICATIONS LIMITED

A Read With Me Story Book

Brer Rabbit

Brer Fox

Cupboard

Brer Bear

Pictured on this page are some of the animals and things featured in this story. Encourage the children to whom you are reading to SEE and SAY the word for each.

Then, as you read the story to them and you come to a picture in place of a word, pause each time for the children to SEE and SAY.

Children love to participate in this kind of storytelling and the SEE and SAY storybooks will become their first choice for reading fun.

Scary Monster

Foxes

ISBN 1-84135-083-4

Copyright © 2001 Award Publications Limited

First published 2001 by Award Publications Limited,
27 Longford Street, London NW1 3DZ

Printed in Malaysia

Honey

Rope

Leaves

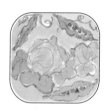

Green Peas and Lettuces

Stick

Fence

BRER RABBIT
AND THE HONEY POT

Brer Rabbit was a clever little fellow but sometimes he was naughty. One day he saw  going out for a walk.

"I will go and look in 's house to see if I can find something to eat in his s," said .

 skipped along to 's house. When he got there, he pushed open the  and went into 's kitchen. He looked around.

"I can only see bread and cheese on the ," said , "and I don't like bread and cheese. I wonder if  keeps any food in that .

"Perhaps there are some

or some nice juicy   ."

So  stood on a stool and

opened the .

"I can only see  and ."

he said to himself, "but I can see

some on the top of the ."

 had to reach up

to get the , but the pot

tipped over. Poor  fell

off the stool with the sticky

 all over him.

"I like ," thought , "but not all over me! If I go out, the bees will chase me because they will think I have stolen their . If I stay here,  will catch me."

He licked himself all over but he couldn't get the  off. So  decided that he would run into

the woods and roll in the  to

rub off all the  .

    This wasn't a good idea, because

the  got stuck all over him.

All the little animals ran away when

they saw  coming.

"They think I am a ," he

thought. Then he had an idea how

he could scare his old enemy, .

 hid behind a  and

waited. When  came along,

 jumped out, waving his arms so

that the  made a swishy noise.

"Grrr," he shouted, "I'm a .

I eat bad  for my dinner!"

"Help, help!" shouted  and

he ran away as fast as he could go.

Now, whenever  sees ,

he always calls out to him, "Mind the

 doesn't get you!"

BRER RABBIT AND
BRER BEAR

One day  looked over the

at 's vegetable garden.

"I spy lots of 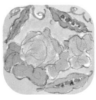," said .

He squeezed through a hole at the

bottom of the  and ate as many

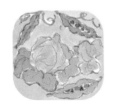 as he could.

 was very angry when he

found out that someone had been

eating some of his 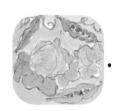.

"I'm sure the thief was ," said

. "I must set a trap by this hole

in the  to catch him."

He made a clever trap with a piece

of  tied to a bent  branch and fixed to a  .

"Now I shall catch
 when he comes
back to steal my ,"
said , laughing.

 came back the next day to eat some more of the 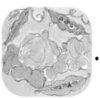. As  crawled through the hole in the , he was caught by 's trap. The was knocked away, the branch sprang back and poor  was left dangling high up on the end of the .

"Oh dear!" thought ,  "  has really caught me this time!" Then he saw  coming along the road and he had an idea.

"Hello, ," said . "What are you doing up there in that ?"

"  is paying me a pound a minute to frighten the  away from his  ," said  . "But I am very busy, so if you would like to have my job, you can take my place on the end of this  ."

 thought it would be very

nice to earn some money, so he

untied the  and helped

to get down from the . Then

 tied the round his waist

so that he could take 's place.

When he was sure that was

up in the ,  picked as

many  as he could carry and

hurried away through the hole in the

When  came back he saw

 in his trap.

"So you're the thief who has been

stealing my 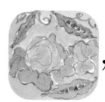," he shouted. "I

will teach you a lesson with my big

 !"

So silly  got into trouble

instead of clever  .

"It's not always the largest people

who have the biggest and cleverest

brains!" said , laughing as he ate

the 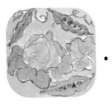.